Our
Christian Family
Journal

This book has been lovingly compiled by

_____

for the

_____

family

Our Christian Family Journal

TRINITY™

By QuillMark™
A division of Random House, Inc.
New York

Our special thanks to the following authors and spokespersons
for their permission to use the quotations
appearing in this book: Elizabeth Asquith Bibesco,
Edwin Land, Dwight D. Eisenhower, courtesy
of Reader's Digest Press, Inc., New York, NY; Faith Baldwin,
Facing Toward the Spring; George Bernard Shaw, *The Doctor's
Dilemma;* and Rabbi Julius Gordon, *Your Sense of Humor.*

Design by Antler & Baldwin Design Group

Manufactured in the United States of America
98765432   24689753   23456789
First Edition
ISBN: 0-866-81718-2

CONTENTS

Family Today

Family History

Christian Milestones

Family Traditions

Special Family Events

Family Facts

Family Highlights

Family File

Photographs

We hope you find this family journal a pleasure to complete and fascinating to read with your family through the years.

We have divided this journal into different sections to make it easy for you to record those pieces of information you have gathered about your family. These sections are for recording current information about your family, past history and traditions, favorite recipes and stories too good to forget. We also thought you would want to record family milestones, health history and sentimental memories from your past. There is a section to record vacations, activities, clubs, hobbies and family reunions. You will also have a place to record current information to keep at your fingertips such as insurance policy numbers, investments, important documents, and a place to figure a budget. You may also record in this section information such as names, addresses, birthdays, anniversaries and phone numbers. Finally, we have provided a section where you can attach family photographs.

Your family journal will be a record of your family that reaches from the past to the present and on into the future. It is our hope that this book begins a loving family tradition, passed down from one generation to the next.

"**A** perfect home is a
hearth and a horizon."
Adapted from Elizabeth
Asquith Bibesco
Reader's Digest, October, 1950

FAMILY TODAY

(place family photograph here)

Our Family Portrait

Introducing Our Family

Before you begin researching your family's history, let's take a look at who and where your family is today.

Father

Full name

Birthdate   Birthplace

Brief background

Mother

Maiden name

Birthdate   Birthplace

Brief background

Marriage

Date   Place

By

Witnesses

Children

Full name

Birthdate   Birthplace

Brief background

Marriage

Their children

Full name

Birthdate   Birthplace

Brief background

Marriage

Their children

Full name

Birthdate   Birthplace

Brief background

Marriage

Their children

Full name

Birthdate   Birthplace

Brief background

_____

_____

_____

Marriage

Their children

_____

_____

Notes

_____

_____

_____

_____

_____

_____

_____

_____

_____

_____

_____

_____

_____

_____

_____

_____

_____

(place photograph here)

Our Home

Here is a place to keep all kinds of miscellaneous information about your home for quick reference.

Address
_____

County _____ Township _____

School system _____

Voting district _____

Date we moved in _____

Realtor _____ Title company _____

Legal description of home & property
_____
_____
_____

Plot number _____ Mortgage company __

Description

_____
_____
_____
_____
_____
_____
_____
_____
_____
_____
_____

Our Hometown

Here is a place to keep notes about special people and places in your neighborhood and hometown. Maybe there have been special community events that you would like to record and remember.

_____
_____
_____
_____
_____
_____
_____
_____
_____
_____
_____
_____
_____
_____
_____
_____
_____

Vocations & Avocations

Careers sometimes are arrived at by direct means, sometimes indirect. Note here what jobs members of your family hold and what hobbies you pursue. Such things may change in time, but their importance remains.

Family Pets

Pets are very much a part of the American family tradition. Here is a place to keep notes on your very special family members.

Name

Breed or description

Born on   Date received

Pet's background

Interesting notes

Veterinarian   Telephone

Name

Breed or description

Born on   Date received

Pet's background

Interesting notes

Veterinarian   Telephone

Name

Breed or description

Born on   Date received

Pet's background

Interesting notes

Veterinarian   Telephone

Our Cars

There's a lot to remember about family cars these days with insurance, registration and maintenance information. The following page can serve as your family's collection point for these details.

Make _____ Model _____

Year _____ Color _____

Purchase date _____ Purchased from _____

Registration number _____

Serial number _____

Maintenance records are kept _____

Insurer _____ Telephone _____

Make _____ Model _____

Year _____ Color _____

Purchase date _____ Purchased from _____

Registration number _____

Serial number _____

Maintenance records are kept _____

Insurer _____

"There are few families in the world that do not reach at one end of the line to the highest prince, and at the other end, to simpletons."

Jean De La Bruyere
Caractères, 1688

FAMILY HISTORY

An Introduction to Genealogy

As interesting and multifaceted as your life is today, so were the lives of your ancestors. When you begin tracing your ancestral line, you'll find out a lot more about your family than names, birthdates, and places where they lived. You'll be discovering your heritage and researching American history firsthand. As you gather facts, you'll begin to see glimpses of past personalities. Individual heroics, humor, and shadowy stories about your ancestors may emerge. Always, the bits and pieces of information you uncover show your ancestors as very human and their lives often poignant. Your research, then, becomes a very definite link with the past as well as a fascinating hobby.

In today's increasingly mobile society, it can be difficult to keep track of all your present relatives and even more so those of the past. The genealogy charts you will find in this chapter can help you begin the organization of an ongoing, continually updated record of your family. These charts are not intended to provide a comprehensive ancestral history. Their purpose is to serve as an interesting tool from which you can discover information about your famiy. If you wish, you can always continue the research and use these genealogical charts as your beginning groundwork.

The family charts in this book go back four generations on both the paternal and maternal sides of your family, including brothers, sisters, aunts and uncles. In some cases, you may only be able to fill in some of the blanks on these charts and in others, you may be able to trace family lines back even farther than the four generations we've allowed room for. If you find you need more space for information, make a note beside the particular family line you are tracing and complete your findings on the blank page following each chart.

To begin your research, write down all you know about your immediate family. Begin gathering new information by talking to older relatives about what they remember and using the sources around home to which you have immediate access. Family Bibles, photograph albums, old letters and diaries can supply you with information. There are many local sources of data that are also easily obtained. Try your local library for microfilmed records and old newspapers. Your courthouse contains county records and historical books and documents, as does your local historical society. Old city directories can supply information about wills, deeds, land purchases and more. Some other places you might want to research are:

The State Board of Health (birth and death records), The State Library (voting records, land deeds, marriages and death records), State Archives (military records) and The National Archives at Washington, D.C. Going through cemetary indexes can be helpful, and individual gravesites (usually the older ones) often contain verses or statements about the individual.

As you gather family history, remember to fill in your charts with pencil at first. It is very likely that, as you continue to research your roots, you will find some inconsistencies in the data you collect. Always record an individual by his or her full name rather than a nickname or initials whenever possible. This will help you identify the correct information on this person since legal documents are most likely recorded by full given name. Remember to record women by their maiden names, to more easily trace their lineage. Children should be listed in the order of their birth.

When completed, you family tree will provide a fascinating look at your heritage and may well become a cherished family record to pass on to your descendants in the years to come.

For more in-depth genealogy studies, the following books and pamphlets may provide you with helpful information.

1. Lindner, Bill R. *How to Trace Your Family History, A Basic Guide to Genealogy.* Everest House, New York, N.Y. 1978.
2. Doane, Gilbert H. *Searching for Your Ancestors.* University of Minnesota Press, Minneapolis, Minnesota, 1974
3. "The Genie Kit," a guide to basic information on genealogy and holdings in the National Archives. Write for free pamphlet: National Archives and Records Service, Central Reference Division, Washington, D.C., 20408.
4. Write for free information on birth and death records, marriage records, and divorce records: The National Center for Health Statistics, 3700 East-West Highway, Room 157, Central Building, Hayattsville, Maryland 20782.

Father's Family Tree

Father

Name
_____

Birthdate _____ Birthplace _____

Business or profession _____

_____

Place of residence _____

Married to _____ Date of marriage _____

Children, birthdates _____

_____

_____

_____

_____

Father's Parents

Father's name
_____

Mother's name
_____

Birthdate _____

Birthdate _____

Birthplace _____

Birthplace _____

Business or profession _____

Business or profession _____

Place of residence _____

Date of marriage _____

Children, birthdates _____

_____

_____

_____

_____

Father's Siblings

Name

Birthdate

Birthplace

Business or profession

Place of residence

Married to   Date of marriage

Children, birthdates

Name

Birthdate

Birthplace

Business or profession

Place of residence

Married to   Date of marriage

Children, birthdates

Name

Birthdate

Birthplace

Business or profession

Place of residence

Married to   Date of marriage

Children, birthdates

Name

Birthdate

Birthplace

Business or profession

Place of residence

Married to   Date of marriage

Children, birthdates

Name

Birthdate

Birthplace

Business or profession

Place of residence

Married to   Date of marriage

Children, birthdates

Name

Birthdate

Birthplace

Business or profession

Place of residence

Married to   Date of marriage

Children, birthdates

Father's Grandparents

Grandfather's name _____

Birthdate _____ Date died

Birthplace _____

Business or profession _____

Place of residence _____

Date of marriage _____

Children, birthdates _____

_____

_____

_____

Grandmother's name _____

Birthdate _____ Date died

Birthplace _____

Business or profession _____

Grandfather's name _____

Birthdate _____ Date died

Birthplace _____

Business or profession _____

Place of residence _____

Date of marriage _____

Children, birthdates _____

_____

_____

_____

Grandmother's name _____

Birthdate _____ Date died

Birthplace _____

Business or profession _____

Siblings

_____

_____

_____

_____

_____

_____

_____

Siblings

_____

_____

_____

_____

_____

_____

_____

Father's Great-Grandparents

Great-Grandfather's name

Birthdate _____ Date died

Business or profession

Place of residence

Children, birthdates

Great-Grandmother's name

Birthdate _____ Date died

Business or profession

Date of marriage

Great-Grandfather's name

Birthdate _____ Date died

Business or profession

Place of residence

Children, birthdates

Great-Grandmother's name

Birthdate _____ Date died

Business or profession

Date of marriage

Great-Grandfather's name

Birthdate _____ Date died

Business or profession

Place of residence

Children, birthdates

Great-Grandmother's name

Birthdate _____ Date died

Business or profession

Date of marriage

Great-Grandfather's name

Birthdate _____ Date died

Business or profession

Place of residence

Children, birthdates

Great-Grandmother's name

Birthdate _____ Date died

Business or profession

Date of marriage

Father's Great-Great-Grandparents

Great-Great-Grandfather's name

Birthdate   Date died

Birthplace

Business or profession

Place of residence

Children, birthdates

Great-Great-Grandmother's name

Birthdate   Date died

Birthplace

Business or profession

Date of marriage

Great-Great-Grandfather's name

Birthdate   Date died

Birthplace

Business or profession

Place of residence

Children, birthdates

Great-Great-Grandmother's name

Birthdate   Date died

Birthplace

Business or profession

Date of marriage

Great-Great-Grandfather's name

Birthdate   Date died

Birthplace

Business or profession

Place of residence

Children, birthdates

Great-Great-Grandmother's name

Birthdate   Date died

Birthplace

Business or profession

Date of marriage

Great-Great-Grandfather's name

Birthdate   Date died

Birthplace

Business or profession

Place of residence

Children, birthdates

Great-Great-Grandmother's name

Birthdate   Date died

Birthplace

Business or profession

Date of marriage

Father's Great-Great-Grandparents

Great-Great-Grandfather's name

Birthdate   Date died

Birthplace

Business or profession

Place of residence

Children, birthdates

Great-Great-Grandmother's name

Birthdate   Date died

Birthplace

Business or profession

Date of marriage

Great-Great-Grandfather's name

Birthdate   Date died

Birthplace

Business or profession

Place of residence

Children, birthdates

Great-Great-Grandmother's name

Birthdate   Date died

Birthplace

Business or profession

Date of marriage

Great-Great-Grandfather's name

Birthdate   Date died

Birthplace

Business or profession

Place of residence

Children, birthdates

Great-Great-Grandmother's name

Birthdate   Date died

Birthplace

Business or profession

Date of marriage

Great-Great-Grandfather's name

Birthdate   Date died

Birthplace

Business or profession

Place of residence

Children, birthdates

Great-Great-Grandmother's name

Birthdate   Date died

Birthplace

Business or profession

Date of marriage

Notes

Notes

31

Mother's Family Tree

Mother

Name
_____

Birthdate _____ Birthplace _____

Business or profession _____

_____

Place of residence _____

Married to _____ Date of marriage _____

Children, birthdates _____

_____

_____

_____

_____

_____

Mother's Parents

Father's name	**Mother's name**
Birthdate	Birthdate
Birthplace	Birthplace
Business or profession	Business or profession
Place of residence	
Date of marriage	
Children, birthdates	

Mother's Siblings

Name

Birthdate

Birthplace

Business or profession

Place of residence

Married to   Date of marriage

Children, birthdates

Name

Birthdate

Birthplace

Business or profession

Place of residence

Married to   Date of marriage

Children, birthdates

Name

Birthdate

Birthplace

Business or profession

Place of residence

Married to   Date of marriage

Children, birthdates

Name

Birthdate

Birthplace

Business or profession

Place of residence

Married to   Date of marriage

Children, birthdates

Name

Birthdate

Birthplace

Business or profession

Place of residence

Married to   Date of marriage

Children, birthdates

Name

Birthdate

Birthplace

Business or profession

Place of residence

Married to   Date of marriage

Children, birthdates

Mother's Grandparents

Grandfather's name

Birthdate   Date died

Birthplace

Business or profession

Place of residence

Date of marriage

Children, birthdates

Grandmother's name

Birthdate   Date died

Birthplace

Business or profession

Grandfather's name

Birthdate   Date died

Birthplace

Business or profession

Place of residence

Date of marriage

Children, birthdates

Grandmother's name

Birthdate   Date died

Birthplace

Business or profession

Siblings

Siblings

Mother's Great-Grandparents

Great-Grandfather's name

Birthdate   Date died

Business or profession

Place of residence

Children, birthdates

Great-Grandmother's name

Birthdate   Date died

Business or profession

Date of marriage

Great-Grandfather's name

Birthdate   Date died

Business or profession

Place of residence

Children, birthdates

Great-Grandmother's name

Birthdate   Date died

Business or profession

Date of marriage

Great-Grandfather's name

Birthdate   Date died

Business or profession

Place of residence

Children, birthdates

Great-Grandmother's name

Birthdate   Date died

Business or profession

Date of marriage

Great-Grandfather's name

Birthdate   Date died

Business or profession

Place of residence

Children, birthdates

Great-Grandmother's name

Birthdate   Date died

Business or profession

Date of marriage

Mother's Great-Great-Grandparents

Great-Great-Grandfather's name

Birthdate _____ Date died

Birthplace

Business or profession

Place of residence

Children, birthdates

Great-Great-Grandmother's name

Birthdate _____ Date died

Birthplace

Business or profession

Date of marriage

Great-Great-Grandfather's name

Birthdate _____ Date died

Birthplace

Business or profession

Place of residence

Children, birthdates

Great-Great-Grandmother's name

Birthdate _____ Date died

Birthplace

Business or profession

Date of marriage

Great-Great-Grandfather's name

Birthdate _____ Date died

Birthplace

Business or profession

Place of residence

Children, birthdates

Great-Great-Grandmother's name

Birthdate _____ Date died

Birthplace

Business or profession

Date of marriage

Great-Great-Grandfather's name

Birthdate _____ Date died

Birthplace

Business or profession

Place of residence

Children, birthdates

Great-Great-Grandmother's name

Birthdate _____ Date died

Birthplace

Business or profession

Date of marriage

Mother's Great-Great-Grandparents

Great-Great-Grandfather's name

Birthdate   Date died

Birthplace

Business or profession

Place of residence

Children, birthdates

Great-Great-Grandmother's name

Birthdate   Date died

Birthplace

Business or profession

Date of marriage

Great-Great-Grandfather's name

Birthdate   Date died

Birthplace

Business or profession

Place of residence

Children, birthdates

Great-Great-Grandmother's name

Birthdate   Date died

Birthplace

Business or profession

Date of marriage

Great-Great-Grandfather's name

Birthdate   Date died

Birthplace

Business or profession

Place of residence

Children, birthdates

Great-Great-Grandmother's name

Birthdate   Date died

Birthplace

Business or profession

Date of marriage

Great-Great-Grandfather's name

Birthdate   Date died

Birthplace

Business or profession

Place of residence

Children, birthdates

Great-Great-Grandmother's name

Birthdate   Date died

Birthplace

Business or profession

Date of marriage

Notes

Notes

Our Children,
the Next Generation

Our Children

Name

Birthdate   Birthplace

Business or profession

Place of residence

Married to   Date of marriage

Comments

Name

Birthdate   Birthplace

Business or profession

Place of residence

Married to   Date of marriage

Comments

Name

Birthdate   Birthplace

Business or profession

Place of residence

Married to   Date of marriage

Comments

Name

Birthdate _____ Birthplace _____

Business or profession _____

Place of residence _____

Married to _____ Date of marriage _____

Comments _____

Our Children's Children

Name _____

Birthdate _____

Birthplace _____

Comments _____

Name _____

Birthdate _____

Birthplace _____

Comments _____

Name _____

Birthdate _____

Birthplace _____

Comments _____

Name _____

Birthdate _____

Birthplace _____

Comments _____

Name _____

Birthdate _____

Birthplace _____

Comments _____

Name _____

Birthdate _____

Birthplace _____

Comments _____

Notes

Notes

Looking Back...

Looking back over the years, there are special moments and places that really bring back the memories. Your homes, pets and cars all signify eras in your life you shared with your family. Here is a place to recall these bits of sentiment.

Remembering Our Homes

Address _____

Resided here from _____ to _____

Recollections _____

_____

_____

Friends and neighbors _____

_____

_____

_____

_____

Address _____

Resided here from _____ to _____

Recollections _____

_____

_____

Friends and neighbors _____

_____

_____

_____

Address

Resided here from   to

Recollections

Friends and neighbors

Address

Resided here from   to

Recollections

Friends and neighbors

Pets to Remember

Name

_____

Breed or description

_____

_____

Span of time pet stayed with us

_____

Special memories

_____

_____

_____

Name

_____

Breed or description

_____

_____

Span of time pet stayed with us

_____

Special memories

_____

_____

_____

Name

_____

Breed or description

_____

_____

Span of time pet stayed with us

_____

Special memories

_____

_____

_____

Name

_____

Breed or description

_____

_____

Span of time pet stayed with us

_____

Special memories

_____

_____

Cars of the Past

Make _____ Model _____ Year _____ Color _____

Date purchased _____ Sold _____

Interesting stories and thoughts about our car

_____

_____

_____

_____

Make _____ Model _____ Year _____ Color _____

Date purchased _____ Sold _____

Interesting stories and thoughts about our car

_____

_____

_____

_____

Make _____ Model _____ Year _____ Color _____

Date purchased _____ Sold _____

Interesting stories and thoughts about our car

_____

_____

_____

_____

Make _____ Model _____ Year _____ Color _____

Date purchased _____ Sold _____

Interesting stories and thoughts about our car

_____

_____

_____

_____

"If instead of a jewel, or
even a flower, we could cast the
gift of a lovely thought into the
heart of another, that would be
giving as the angels must give."

Anonymous

CHRISTIAN
MILESTONES

Our Places of Worship

"Now ye are the body of Christ, and members in particular."

I CORINTHIANS 12:27

Name of our present church
_____

Pastors _____ Dates _____

_____

_____

_____

_____

Past churches _____

_____

_____

_____

Special Services

_____

_____

_____

_____

_____

_____

_____

_____

_____

_____

_____

_____

_____

_____

Outreach Ministry

_____
_____
_____
_____
_____
_____
_____
_____
_____
_____
_____

Church Activities

_____
_____
_____
_____
_____
_____
_____
_____
_____
_____
_____
_____
_____
_____

Weddings

"**B**ut from the beginning of the creation God made them male and female. For this cause shall a man leave his father and mother, and cleave to his wife…so then they are no more twain, but one flesh."

MARK 10:6-8

Names

Date   Church

Officiating Clergy

Notes

Names

Date   Church

Officiating Clergy

Notes

Names

Date   Church

Officiating Clergy

Notes

Names _____

Date _____ Church _____

Officiating Clergy _____

Notes _____

_____

_____

_____

Names _____

Date _____ Church _____

Officiating Clergy _____

Notes _____

_____

_____

_____

Names _____

Date _____ Church _____

Officiating Clergy _____

Notes _____

_____

_____

_____

Names _____

Date _____ Church _____

Officiating Clergy _____

Notes _____

_____

_____

_____

Baptisms

"Therefore we are buried with him by baptism into death: that like as Christ was raised up from the dead by the glory of the Father, even so we also should walk in newness of life."

ROMANS 6:4

Name

Date

Church

Officiating Clergy

Notes

Name

Date

Church

Officiating Clergy

Notes

Name

Date

Church

Officiating Clergy

Notes

Name

Date

Church

Officiating Clergy

Notes

Name

Date

Church

Officiating Clergy

Notes

_____

_____

_____

_____

Name

Date

Church

Officiating Clergy

Notes

_____

_____

_____

_____

Name

Date

Church

Officiating Clergy

Notes

_____

_____

_____

_____

Name

Date

Church

Officiating Clergy

Notes

_____

_____

_____

_____

Name

Date

Church

Officiating Clergy

Notes

_____

_____

_____

_____

Name

Date

Church

Officiating Clergy

Notes

_____

_____

_____

_____

Funerals

"Let not your heart be troubled: ye believe in God, believe also in me. In my Father's house are many mansions: if it were not so, I would have told you. I go to prepare a place for you. And if I go and prepare a place for you, I will come again, and receive you unto myself; that where I am, there ye may be also."

JOHN 14:1-3

Name

Date

Church

Officiating Clergy

Notes

Name

Date

Church

Officiating Clergy

Notes

Name

Date

Church

Officiating Clergy

Notes

Name

Date

Church

Officiating Clergy

Notes

Name

Date

Church

Officiating Clergy

Notes

Name

Date

Church

Officiating Clergy

Notes

Name

Date

Church

Officiating Clergy

Notes

Name

Date

Church

Officiating Clergy

Notes

Name

Date

Church

Officiating Clergy

Notes

Name

Date

Church

Officiating Clergy

Notes

Spiritual Awakenings

"Jesus answered and said unto him, Verily, verily, I say unto thee, Except a man be born again, he cannot see the kingdom of God."

JOHN 3:3

The Born Again Experience

_____

_____

_____

_____

_____

_____

_____

_____

_____

_____

_____

_____

_____

_____

_____

_____

_____

_____

_____

_____

_____

_____

Called to Christian Service

Reaching Others for Christ

Scriptural Influences

"Thy word have I hid in mine heart, that I might not sin against thee."

PSALM 119:11

Here is a place to record verses of Scripture that have caused a major impact on your lives.

Verse References and Quotes

_____

_____

_____

_____

_____

_____

_____

_____

_____

_____

_____

_____

_____

_____

_____

_____

_____

_____

_____

_____

Circumstances and Application

_____
_____
_____
_____
_____
_____
_____
_____
_____
_____
_____
_____
_____
_____
_____
_____
_____
_____
_____
_____
_____
_____
_____
_____
_____
_____
_____
_____
_____

"Thy word is a lamp unto my feet,
and a light unto my path."
PSALMS 119:105

"For the Lord taketh pleasure in his people: he will beautify the meek with salvation."

PSALM 149:4

FAMILY TRADITIONS

Traditions to Keep

Just about every American family celebrates occasions important to them in ways uniquely their own. These family traditions often begin generations back in family history, the product of religious beliefs, community practices, or concepts originating from your ancestors' native lands.

_____

_____

_____

_____

_____

_____

_____

_____

_____

_____

_____

_____

_____

_____

_____

_____

_____

_____

_____

_____

_____

_____

Holiday Traditions

Over the years, many families have developed special ways of marking holidays. Use this space to capture memories about your particular celebrations. You may want to include occasions such as Christmas, Easter, Mother's Day, Father's Day, Memorial Day, July Fourth and Thanksgiving.

Family Heirlooms

Your family "heirlooms" may not necessarily be worth a small fortune. Their meaning to you is what makes them special. Here is a place to record the date, occasion and sentiment behind each piece.

Item _____

Description _____
_____

History _____
_____
_____

Value _____

Item _____

Description _____
_____

History _____
_____
_____

Value _____

Item _____

Description _____
_____

History _____
_____
_____

Value _____

Item _____

Description _____
_____

History _____
_____
_____

Value _____

Item _____

Description _____
_____

History _____
_____
_____

Value _____

Item _____

Description _____
_____

History _____
_____
_____

Value _____

Item

Description

History

Value

Item

Description

History

Value

Item

Description

History

Value

Item

Description

History

Value

Item

Description

History

Value

Item

Description

History

Value

Favorite Recipes

If you are like most families, you have some recipes that have become family favorites over the years. Preserve your family's favorites here for easy reference today and an interesting record for the future.

Recipe

A favorite of _____ Serves _____

Ingredients

_____

_____

_____

Directions

_____

_____

_____

_____

_____

Recipe

A favorite of _____ Serves _____

Ingredients

_____

_____

Directions

_____

_____

_____

_____

_____

Recipe

A favorite of   Serves

Ingredients

Directions

Recipe

A favorite of   Serves

Ingredients

Directions

Recipe

A favorite of   Serves

Ingredients

Directions

Stories to Remember & Pass On

Here are the stories and humorous anecdotes you want to remember…notes on growing up in years gone by, current happenings, perhaps even the recollections of your parents and grandparents. Jotting down the approximate date and the name of the person to whom you attribute the story will make this chapter a cherished family possession.

_____

_____

_____

_____

_____

_____

_____

_____

_____

_____

_____

_____

_____

_____

_____

_____

_____

_____

_____

_____

_____

"Time is a dressmaker
specializing in alterations."
Faith Baldwin
Facing Toward the Spring

SPECIAL
FAMILY EVENTS

Special Family Events

As you look back, there are certain times and occasions in every family's history that stand apart as turning points. Your family's milestones might include such major events as graduations, baptisms, entering the military, the appearance of a first grandchild, or very special events of personal significance to your family alone. Whatever your family's milestones are, here is a place to note the occasions.

"Use your health, even to the point of wearing it out. That is what it is for. Spend all you have before you die; and do not outlive yourself.

George Bernard Shaw
The Doctor's Dilemma

FAMILY FACTS

Our Family Health History

Keeping track of your family's health history can help you predict health tendencies and traits. Begin filling in the chart with information about yourself and your immediate family. Ask your grandparents, aunts and uncles to help you trace health information.

_____
_____
_____
_____
_____
_____
_____
_____
_____
_____
_____
_____
_____
_____
_____
_____
_____
_____
_____
_____
_____

Relative	Allergies	Cancer	Diabetes	Heart	Stroke	Ulcers	Other	Cause of death, age

Health Record

Over the preceding two pages, you have completed information noting health problems peculiar to your family. This section may serve as a preventative maintenance record for quick and accurate health reference for your family today.

Name (Father)

Physical Examinations				Immunizations	
Date	Doctor	Pulse	Blood pressure	Date	Vaccine
Date	Doctor	Pulse	Blood pressure	Date	Vaccine
Date	Doctor	Pulse	Blood pressure	Date	Vaccine
Date	Doctor	Pulse	Blood pressure	Date	Vaccine
Date	Doctor	Pulse	Blood pressure	Date	Vaccine

Name (Mother)

Physical Examinations				Immunizations	
Date	Doctor	Pulse	Blood pressure	Date	Vaccine
Date	Doctor	Pulse	Blood pressure	Date	Vaccine
Date	Doctor	Pulse	Blood pressure	Date	Vaccine
Date	Doctor	Pulse	Blood pressure	Date	Vaccine
Date	Doctor	Pulse	Blood pressure	Date	Vaccine

Name (Child)

Physical Examinations				Immunizations	
Date	Doctor	Pulse	Blood pressure	Date	Vaccine
Date	Doctor	Pulse	Blood pressure	Date	Vaccine
Date	Doctor	Pulse	Blood pressure	Date	Vaccine
Date	Doctor	Pulse	Blood pressure	Date	Vaccine
Date	Doctor	Pulse	Blood pressure	Date	Vaccine

Name (Child)

	Physical Examinations					Immunizations

Date	Doctor		Pulse	Blood pressure	Date	Vaccine
Date	Doctor		Pulse	Blood pressure	Date	Vaccine
Date	Doctor		Pulse	Blood pressure	Date	Vaccine
Date	Doctor		Pulse	Blood pressure	Date	Vaccine
Date	Doctor		Pulse	Blood pressure	Date	Vaccine

Name (Child)

	Physical Examinations					Immunizations

Date	Doctor		Pulse	Blood pressure	Date	Vaccine
Date	Doctor		Pulse	Blood pressure	Date	Vaccine
Date	Doctor		Pulse	Blood pressure	Date	Vaccine
Date	Doctor		Pulse	Blood pressure	Date	Vaccine
Date	Doctor		Pulse	Blood pressure	Date	Vaccine

Name (Child)

	Physical Examinations					Immunizations

Date	Doctor		Pulse	Blood pressure	Date	Vaccine
Date	Doctor		Pulse	Blood pressure	Date	Vaccine
Date	Doctor		Pulse	Blood pressure	Date	Vaccine
Date	Doctor		Pulse	Blood pressure	Date	Vaccine
Date	Doctor		Pulse	Blood pressure	Date	Vaccine

Notes

Children's Growth Chart

Children take great delight in comparing their height and weight at various times during their growing years. You might want to begin the practice of measuring each child on his or her birthday, or on the same day each year. These growth patterns will be even more interesting to compare and assess if you can include corresponding information on parents' and grandparents' growth.

Name

At birth	Length or height	Weight	8	Height	Weight
6 months	Length or height	Weight	9	Height	Weight
1 year	Height	Weight	10	Height	Weight
2	Height	Weight	11	Height	Weight
3	Height	Weight	12	Height	Weight
4	Height	Weight	13	Height	Weight
5	Height	Weight	14	Height	Weight
6	Height	Weight	15	Height	Weight
7	Height	Weight	16	Height	Weight

Name

At birth	Length or height	Weight	8	Height	Weight
6 months	Length or height	Weight	9	Height	Weight
1 year	Height	Weight	10	Height	Weight
2	Height	Weight	11	Height	Weight
3	Height	Weight	12	Height	Weight
4	Height	Weight	13	Height	Weight
5	Height	Weight	14	Height	Weight
6	Height	Weight	15	Height	Weight
7	Height	Weight	16	Height	Weight

Name

At birth	Length or height	Weight	8	Height	Weight
6 months	Length or height	Weight	9	Height	Weight
1 year	Height	Weight	10	Height	Weight
2	Height	Weight	11	Height	Weight
3	Height	Weight	12	Height	Weight
4	Height	Weight	13	Height	Weight
5	Height	Weight	14	Height	Weight
6	Height	Weight	15	Height	Weight
7	Height	Weight	16	Height	Weight

Name

At birth	Length or height	Weight	8	Height	Weight
6 months	Length or height	Weight	9	Height	Weight
1 year	Height	Weight	10	Height	Weight
2	Height	Weight	11	Height	Weight
3	Height	Weight	12	Height	Weight
4	Height	Weight	13	Height	Weight
5	Height	Weight	14	Height	Weight
6	Height	Weight	15	Height	Weight
7	Height	Weight	16	Height	Weight

Notes

"Traveling may be one of two things—an experience we shall always remember, or an experience which, alas, we shall never forget."

Rabbi Julius Gordon
Your Sense of Humor

FAMILY HIGHLIGHTS

Vacations & Travel

Here is a place to capture your memories of those favorite family vacations.

_____

_____

_____

_____

_____

_____

_____

_____

_____

_____

_____

_____

_____

_____

_____

_____

_____

_____

_____

_____

_____

_____

_____

_____

Activities, Clubs & Hobbies

Chances are that each member of your family is involved in an activity of some sort, very special to him. These clubs and associations will change over the years but their importance related to personal growth and social change will remain.

Family Reunions
& Friendly Gatherings

Family reunions and friendly gatherings are a great American tradition. Note those that have been important to your family, past and present. Remember too, that you can gather important information about your family ancestry (to help you fill in the second chapter) at these occasions.

"You need only provide your family with one sound investment—let it be enthusiasm."

Anonymous

FAMILY FILE

Insurance

Keep current information on your family's life, health and automobile insurance policies. Your insurance agent can help you fill in any information that you aren't sure about.

Life Insurance

Type of policy
_____

Amount of coverage
_____

_____

_____

Insurance agent
_____

Telephone
_____

Amount of payment
_____

Due date
_____

Where policy is kept
_____

Maturity date (if applicable)
_____

Notes
_____

_____

_____

_____

_____

_____

_____

_____

_____

_____

_____

_____

Health Insurance

Type of policy

Amount of coverage

Insurance agent

Telephone

Amount of payment

Due date

Where policy is kept

Maturity date (if applicable)

Notes

Automobile Insurance

Type of policy

Amount of coverage

Insurance agent

Telephone

Amount of payment

Due date

Where policy is kept

Maturity date (if applicable)

Notes

Real Estate

Your family's real estate includes more than just your home. Record as much information as you can in this section about any land, home, condominium, or property interest your family has.

Legal description of property
_____
_____
_____

Plot or lot number
_____

Buildings on property, description
_____
_____

Realtor _____ Telephone _____

Purchase price _____ Purchase date _____

Present value, date
_____

Property taxes
_____

Zoning information
_____

Location of important documents
_____

Notes
_____
_____
_____
_____
_____
_____
_____
_____
_____
_____

Legal description of property

Plot or lot number

Buildings on property, description

Realtor   Telephone

Purchase price   Purchase date

Present value, date

Property taxes

Zoning information

Location of important documents

Notes

Home improvements, dates

Landscaping, dates

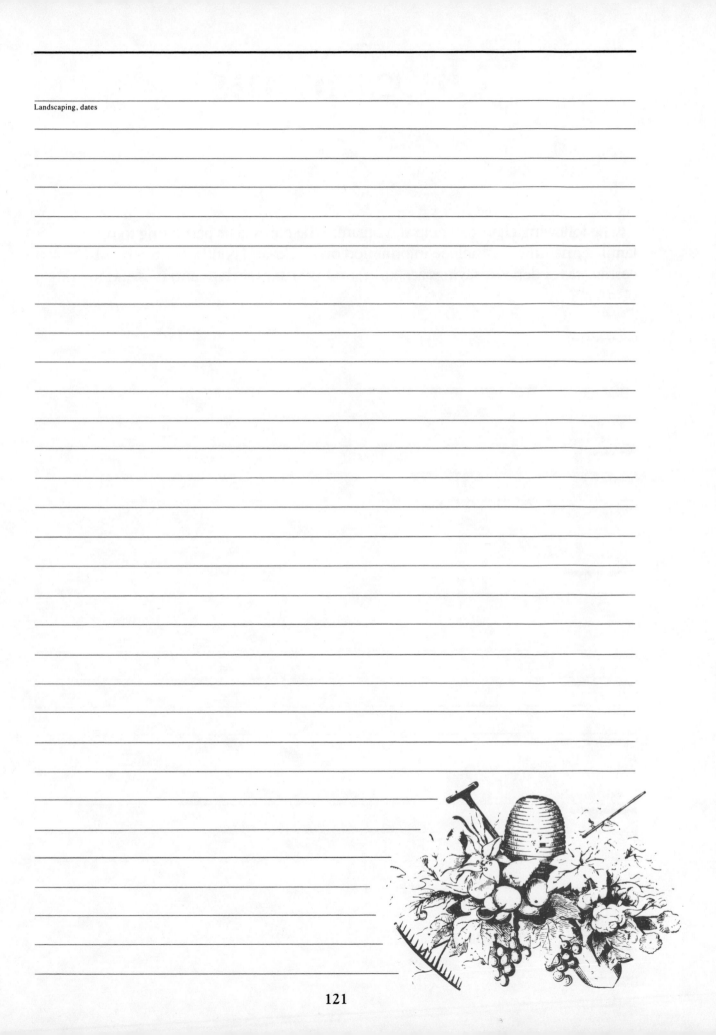

Investments

The following chart can help you organize the particulars pertaining to your family's investments. Include information on stocks and bonds, savings bonds, certificates of deposit, savings accounts, and valuables such as antiques and works of art.

Item/description

Company or title

Identifying number

Present value

Location of papers/item

Item/description

Company or title

Identifying number

Present value

Location of papers/item

Item/description

Company or title

Identifying number

Present value

Location of papers/item

Item/description

Company or title

Identifying number

Present value

Location of papers/item

Item/description

Company or title

Identifying number

Present value

Location of papers/item

Item/description

Company or title

Identifying number

Present value

Location of papers/item

Item/description

Company or title

Identifying number

Present value

Location of papers/item

Item/description

Company or title

Identifying number

Present value

Location of papers/item

Item/description

Company or title

Identifying number

Present value

Location of papers/item

Item/description

Company or title

Identifying number

Present value

Location of papers/item

Item/description

Company or title

Identifying number

Present value

Location of papers/item

Item/description

Company or title

Identifying number

Present value

Location of papers/item

Item/description

Company or title

Identifying number

Present value

Location of papers/item

Item/description

Company or title

Identifying number

Present value

Location of papers/item

Item/description

Company or title

Identifying number

Present value

Location of papers/item

Important Documents

Have you ever thought about what could happen if you misplaced your wallet? You carry a lot more information around with you every day than you could begin to remember. Here is a place to help you systemize your charge cards, checking and savings accounts, and other documents.

Checking account number	Bank	Telephone
Savings account number	Bank	Telephone
Safety deposit box	Bank	Telephone
Driver's license number/Social Security number		
Other		

Credit Cards

Name of card

Card number

Name of issuing company

Name of cardholder

Credit line

In case of loss notify

Name of card

Card number

Name of issuing company

Name of cardholder

Credit line

In case of loss notify

Name of card

Card number

Name of issuing company

Name of cardholder

Credit line

In case of loss notify

Name of card

Card number

Name of issuing company

Name of cardholder

Credit line

In case of loss notify

Name of card

Card number

Name of issuing company

Name of cardholder

Credit line

In case of loss notify

Name of card

Card number

Name of issuing company

Name of cardholder

Credit line

In case of loss notify

Name of card

Card number

Name of issuing company

Name of cardholder

Credit line

In case of loss notify

Name of card

Card number

Name of issuing company

Name of cardholder

Credit line

In case of loss notify

Appliances

Appliance

Where and when purchased

Serial number

Warranty information

Appliance

Where and when purchased

Serial number

Warranty information

Appliance

Where and when purchased

Serial number

Warranty information

Appliance

Where and when purchased

Serial number

Warranty information

Appliance

Where and when purchased

Serial number

Warranty information

Appliance

Where and when purchased

Serial number

Warranty information

Our Family Budget

Y ou may want to use this section to help plan your family's budget and then compare it to your actual costs. It is best to do this on a month-to-month basis, so we have provided you with a one-year calendar. In the years to come, it will be interesting to see just what prices your family was accustomed to paying for heat, electricity, food, insurance, gas, and more. And to help you plan ahead, these charts could give you a more accurate idea of your cost of living.

Yearly Expenditures

_____

_____

_____

_____

_____

_____

_____

_____

_____

Monthly Expenditures: January

Rent/Mortgage	Projected	Actual		Medical expenses	Projected	Actual
Heat	Projected	Actual		Automobile expenses	Projected	Actual
Electricity	Projected	Actual		Appliances/Furniture	Projected	Actual
Water	Projected	Actual		Recreation	Projected	Actual
Telephone	Projected	Actual		Other	Projected	Actual
Food	Projected	Actual				
Clothing	Projected	Actual				
Life insurance	Projected	Actual				
Health insurance	Projected	Actual				

February

Rent/Mortgage	Projected	Actual		Medical expenses	Projected	Actual
Heat	Projected	Actual		Automobile expenses	Projected	Actual
Electricity	Projected	Actual		Appliances/Furniture	Projected	Actual
Water	Projected	Actual		Recreation	Projected	Actual
Telephone	Projected	Actual		Other	Projected	Actual
Food	Projected	Actual				
Clothing	Projected	Actual				
Life insurance	Projected	Actual				
Health insurance	Projected	Actual				

March

Rent/Mortgage	Projected	Actual		Medical expenses	Projected	Actual
Heat	Projected	Actual		Automobile expenses	Projected	Actual
Electricity	Projected	Actual		Appliances/Furniture	Projected	Actual
Water	Projected	Actual		Recreation	Projected	Actual
Telephone	Projected	Actual		Other	Projected	Actual
Food	Projected	Actual				
Clothing	Projected	Actual				
Life insurance	Projected	Actual				
Health insurance	Projected	Actual				

April

Rent/Mortgage	Projected	Actual		Medical expenses	Projected	Actual
Heat	Projected	Actual		Automobile expenses	Projected	Actual
Electricity	Projected	Actual		Appliances/Furniture	Projected	Actual
Water	Projected	Actual		Recreation	Projected	Actual
Telephone	Projected	Actual		Other	Projected	Actual
Food	Projected	Actual				
Clothing	Projected	Actual				
Life insurance	Projected	Actual				
Health insurance	Projected	Actual				

May

Rent/Mortgage	Projected	Actual		Medical expenses	Projected	Actual
Heat	Projected	Actual		Automobile expenses	Projected	Actual
Electricity	Projected	Actual		Appliances/Furniture	Projected	Actual
Water	Projected	Actual		Recreation	Projected	Actual
Telephone	Projected	Actual		Other	Projected	Actual
Food	Projected	Actual				
Clothing	Projected	Actual				
Life insurance	Projected	Actual				
Health insurance	Projected	Actual				

June

Rent/Mortgage	Projected	Actual		Medical expenses	Projected	Actual
Heat	Projected	Actual		Automobile expenses	Projected	Actual
Electricity	Projected	Actual		Appliances/Furniture	Projected	Actual
Water	Projected	Actual		Recreation	Projected	Actual
Telephone	Projected	Actual		Other	Projected	Actual
Food	Projected	Actual				
Clothing	Projected	Actual				
Life insurance	Projected	Actual				
Health insurance	Projected	Actual				

July

Rent/Mortgage	Projected	Actual	Medical expenses	Projected	Actual
Heat	Projected	Actual	Automobile expenses	Projected	Actual
Electricity	Projected	Actual	Appliances/Furniture	Projected	Actual
Water	Projected	Actual	Recreation	Projected	Actual
Telephone	Projected	Actual	Other	Projected	Actual
Food	Projected	Actual			
Clothing	Projected	Actual			
Life insurance	Projected	Actual			
Health insurance	Projected	Actual			

August

Rent/Mortgage	Projected	Actual	Medical expenses	Projected	Actual
Heat	Projected	Actual	Automobile expenses	Projected	Actual
Electricity	Projected	Actual	Appliances/Furniture	Projected	Actual
Water	Projected	Actual	Recreation	Projected	Actual
Telephone	Projected	Actual	Other	Projected	Actual
Food	Projected	Actual			
Clothing	Projected	Actual			
Life insurance	Projected	Actual			
Health insurance	Projected	Actual			

September

Rent/Mortgage	Projected	Actual	Medical expenses	Projected	Actual
Heat	Projected	Actual	Automobile expenses	Projected	Actual
Electricity	Projected	Actual	Appliances/Furniture	Projected	Actual
Water	Projected	Actual	Recreation	Projected	Actual
Telephone	Projected	Actual	Other	Projected	Actual
Food	Projected	Actual			
Clothing	Projected	Actual			
Life insurance	Projected	Actual			
Health insurance	Projected	Actual			

October

Rent/Mortgage	Projected	Actual		Medical expenses	Projected	Actual
Heat	Projected	Actual		Automobile expenses	Projected	Actual
Electricity	Projected	Actual		Appliances/Furniture	Projected	Actual
Water	Projected	Actual		Recreation	Projected	Actual
Telephone	Projected	Actual		Other	Projected	Actual
Food	Projected	Actual				
Clothing	Projected	Actual				
Life insurance	Projected	Actual				
Health insurance	Projected	Actual				

November

Rent/Mortgage	Projected	Actual		Medical expenses	Projected	Actual
Heat	Projected	Actual		Automobile expenses	Projected	Actual
Electricity	Projected	Actual		Appliances/Furniture	Projected	Actual
Water	Projected	Actual		Recreation	Projected	Actual
Telephone	Projected	Actual		Other	Projected	Actual
Food	Projected	Actual				
Clothing	Projected	Actual				
Life insurance	Projected	Actual				
Health insurance	Projected	Actual				

December

Rent/Mortgage	Projected	Actual		Medical expenses	Projected	Actual
Heat	Projected	Actual		Automobile expenses	Projected	Actual
Electricity	Projected	Actual		Appliances/Furniture	Projected	Actual
Water	Projected	Actual		Recreation	Projected	Actual
Telephone	Projected	Actual		Other	Projected	Actual
Food	Projected	Actual				
Clothing	Projected	Actual				
Life insurance	Projected	Actual				
Health insurance	Projected	Actual				

Notes

The Family Directory

Name

Address

Telephone

Birthday

Anniversary

Name

Address

Telephone

Birthday

Anniversary

Name

Address

Telephone

Birthday

Anniversary

Name

Address

Telephone

Birthday

Anniversary

Name

Address

Telephone

Birthday

Anniversary

Name

Address

Telephone

Birthday

Anniversary

Name

Address

Telephone

Birthday

Anniversary

Name

Address

Telephone

Birthday

Anniversary

Name

Address

Telephone

Birthday

Anniversary

Name

Address

Telephone

Birthday

Anniversary

Name

Address

Telephone

Birthday

Anniversary

Name

Address

Telephone

Birthday

Anniversary

Name

Address

Telephone

Birthday

Anniversary

Name

Address

Telephone

Birthday

Anniversary

Name

Address

Telephone

Birthday

Anniversary

Name

Address

Telephone

Birthday

Anniversary

Name

Address

Telephone

Birthday

Anniversary

Name

Address

Telephone

Birthday

Anniversary

Name

Address

Telephone

Birthday

Anniversary

Name

Address

Telephone

Birthday

Anniversary

Name

Address

Telephone

Birthday

Anniversary

Name

Address

Telephone

Birthday

Anniversary

Name

Address

Telephone

Birthday

Anniversary

Name

Address

Telephone

Birthday

Anniversary

Name

Address

Telephone

Birthday

Anniversary

Name

Address

Telephone

Birthday

Anniversary

Name

Address

Telephone

Birthday

Anniversary

Name

Address

Telephone

Birthday

Anniversary

Name

Address

Telephone

Birthday

Anniversary

Name

Address

Telephone

Birthday

Anniversary

"**P**hotographs can teach
people to look, to feel, to
remember in a way that they
didn't know they could."

Edwin Land
Reader's Digest, January, 1974

PHOTOGRAPHS

Family Photographs

Many families have extensive photo collections. You may want to put special photographs of your family members on the following pages. Provided too are decorative frames for those favorites.